DEATH IN THE ICE

THE MYSTERY OF THE FRANKLIN EXPEDITION

KAREN RYAN

CANADIAN MUSEUM OF HISTORY
MUSÉE CANADIEN DE L'HISTOIRE

Library and Archives Canada
Cataloguing in Publication

Ryan, Karen (Archaeologist), author, organizer
Death in the ice: the mystery of the Franklin
expedition / Karen Ryan.

(Souvenir catalogue series, ISSN 2291-6385; 22)

Catalogue of a touring exhibition held at the
National Maritime Museum in Greenwich from
July 14, 2017 to January 7, 2018, and at the
Canadian Museum of History from March 2
to September 20, 2018.

Issued also in French under title:
Périr dans les glaces.
ISBN 978-0-660-07881-6 (softcover)
Cat. no.: NM23-5/22-2018E

1. Franklin, John, Sir, 1786-1847 –
    Relics – Exhibitions.
2. Erebus (Ship) – Exhibitions.
3. Terror (Ship) – Exhibitions.
4. Inuit – Arctic regions – Exhibitions.
5. Northwest Passage – Discovery and
    exploration – British – Exhibitions.

I.   National Maritime Museum (Great Britain),
     issuing body, host institution.
II. Canadian Museum of History, issuing body,
     host institution.
III. Title.
IV. Series: Souvenir catalogue series; 22.

G660.R93 2018
919.804
C2017-903568-1

Published by the Canadian Museum of History
100 Laurier Street
Gatineau, QC K1A 0M8
historymuseum.ca

Printed and bound in Canada

This work is a souvenir of an exhibition
developed by the Canadian Museum of History
(Gatineau, Canada), in partnership with Parks
Canada Agency and with the National Maritime
Museum (London, United Kingdom), and in
collaboration with the Government of Nunavut
and the Inuit Heritage Trust.

Souvenir Catalogue series, 22
ISSN 2291-6385

CONTENTS

THE
NORTHWEST PASSAGE AND THE FRANKLIN EXPEDITION

In May 1845, when Sir John Franklin left Britain in command of the Royal Navy's most ambitious Northwest Passage expedition, no one could have imagined that one of the world's greatest mysteries was about to unfold.

Only a small portion of the Northwest Passage remained uncharted by Europeans, and confidence in the Expedition's success was high.

After two years without word, however, a desperate search for the men and their ships began.

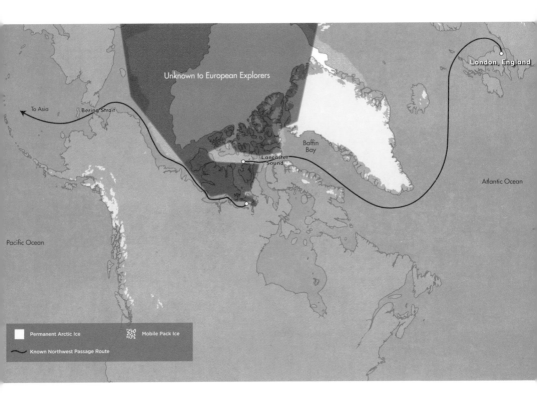

Franklin's Planned Northwest Passage Route

INUIT WITNESSES

Inuit were the last to see the Franklin Expedition, witnessing its end long after HMS *Erebus* and *Terror* entered the Arctic and, from a European perspective, disappeared.

Inuit oral histories preserve many details of the Expedition's final days, including seeing the occupied ships and visiting them once they were abandoned, meeting starving crewmen, and finding their bodies.

This information, first shared with European searchers in 1854, contributed directly to the discovery of *Erebus* and *Terror* in 2014 and 2016, respectively.

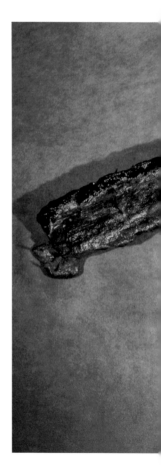

Ship's Wheel
A section of the wheel of *Erebus*, found approximately 30 metres from the wreck in September 2015.

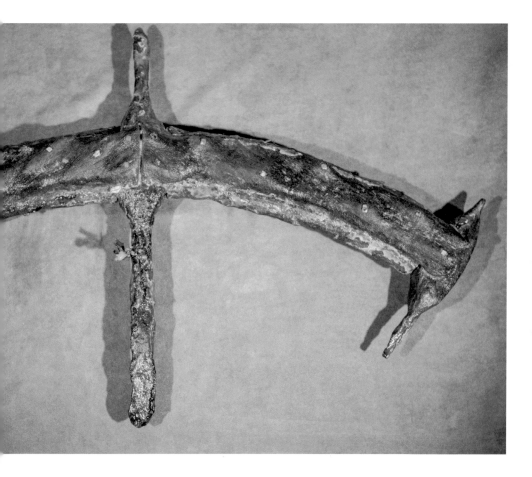

CONFIRMING THE FATE OF THE FRANKLIN EXPEDITION

The first definite news of the Expedition's fate was sent to London by Dr. John Rae, whose Inuit sources indicated the Expedition had been lost northwest of the Back River. When the Admiralty refused to organize a search of this area, Lady Jane Franklin enlisted Francis Leopold McClintock to confirm the Inuit accounts.

Travelling by ship and sledge to the Boothia Peninsula and King William Island between 1857 and 1859, McClintock encountered Inuit who reaffirmed the Expedition's ultimate outcome.

"We learned that two ships had been seen by the natives of King William's Island; *one of them* was seen to sink in deep water; but *the other* was forced on shore by the ice; Oot-loo-lik is the name of the place where she is grounded."

[emphasis in original]

■■■

Inuit testimony relayed to Francis Leopold McClintock in 1859

INUIT TECHNOLOGIES AND FRANKLIN EXPEDITION MATERIALS

Inuit encountered by McClintock had an abundance of European-sourced materials — further proof that the Expedition had met its end nearby.

McClintock purchased a number of Inuit tools, which combined locally available materials with European smelted metals and hardwoods.

Sinew-Backed Bows
The larger bow, collected by McClintock, is made from a single piece of European hardwood. In contrast, the smaller example is made of caribou antler, bone and muskox horn.

Traditional Inuit knives, made of walrus ivory or locally occurring copper, were time-consuming to make and difficult to repair. The Franklin Expedition provided a wealth of new materials, including durable steel blades that were attached to traditionally designed handles.

Knife Made of Two Pieces of Walrus Ivory for Cutting Snow Into Blocks

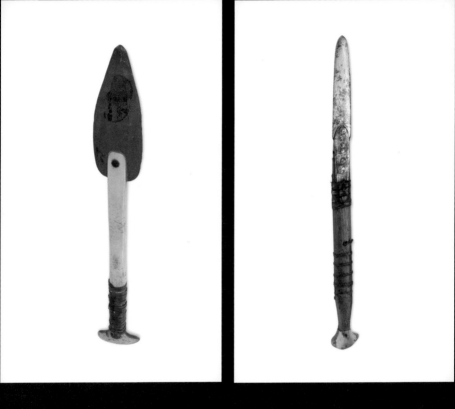

Copper-Bladed Knife Made of Local Materials

Knife With European Steel Blade Riveted to a Handle of Wood and Muskox Horn

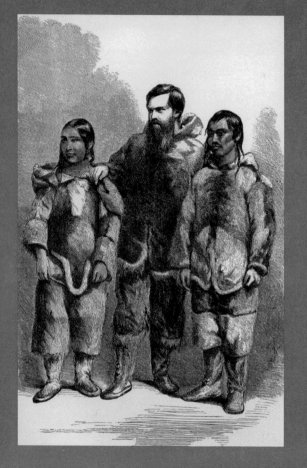

Tookoolito, C. F. Hall, and Ebierbing
From *Life with the Esquimaux: The Narrative of Captain Charles Francis Hall* (1865)

AN EARLIER MEETING - INUIT AND MARTIN FROBISHER

Convinced of the accuracy of Inuit oral histories, and believing some Expedition crewmembers still survived, Charles Francis Hall journeyed to Baffin Island in 1860.

Hall met Taqulittuq (Tookoolito) and Ipivik (Ebierbing). Originally from the Cumberland Sound region of Baffin Island, the two acted as Hall's guides and translators.

Travelling around Frobisher Bay, the three asked local Inuit whether they knew anything about the missing Expedition.

Instead of hearing about Franklin, they learned of a much earlier group of European visitors. Upon arriving at Qallunaat (Kodlunarn) Island — or White Men's Island — Hall saw traces of an old mine, and realized the European remembered by the Inuit was Martin Frobisher, who explored Frobisher Bay beginning in 1576.

Inuit Dolls From Cumberland Sound, Baffin Island
Traditional summer clothing was usually made from ringed-seal skin, which is waterproof and not as warm as caribou skin. An Inuit woman's parka (left) is called an *amauti*.

Oceangoing Kayak and Wooden Paddle
This kayak's wooden frame is 5.5 metres long and covered in sealskin sewn with a waterproof stitch.

Inuit Wooden Model of a European Ship
This carving depicts a type of multi-decked sailing ship common during the 1500s and 1600s. The style of the figure's hat is similar to those worn by European sailors during the same period. The carving was collected from an archaeological site in Amadjuak Bay, on the south coast of Baffin Island.

AN ARCTIC OBSESSION

For more than four centuries, explorers were determined to chart a polar shortcut from the Atlantic to the Pacific. Although many believed it would be easy to find, the Northwest Passage proved to be an ice-filled puzzle in the heart of the Arctic.

Even after it became clear that the Northwest Passage was not a viable trade route, its discovery remained an object of national pride for Britain.

The Admiralty Board Room – Meeting of the Lords of the Admiralty
Engraved by Henry Melville, after Thomas Rowlandson (1843)

A VISION OF ARCTIC EXPLORATION

Sir John Barrow was the Second Secretary to the Admiralty, and a passionate advocate of Arctic exploration. He considered the Northwest Passage "the only interesting discovery that remains in geography."

Under his guidance, nine Royal Navy expeditions were organized, beginning in 1818. Although none was successful, each added to the Admiralty's maps until only a tantalizingly small part of the Northwest Passage remained uncharted by 1845.

"So little now remains to be done ... no reasonable doubt can be entertained ... and no objection with regard to any apprehension of the loss of ships or men."

■■■

Sir John Barrow, Second Secretary to the Admiralty, December 1844

A PASSAGE ALMOST FOUND

One of the earliest Royal Navy expeditions during Sir John Barrow's tenure was its most successful.

William Edward Parry's 1819–1820 expedition sailed three-quarters of the way through the Arctic Archipelago in a single season, fuelling British confidence that the Northwest Passage would soon be completed.

THE LOSS OF HMS FURY

Parry was not as lucky in 1825, when HMS *Fury* was driven ashore by ice near what is now called Fury Beach, on the southeast coast of Somerset Island.

However, *Fury*'s offloaded supplies saved Sir John Ross, whose 1829–1833 Northwest Passage expedition was forced to abandon its ice-beset ship, *Victory*.

Jack Frost and the Fury
Glasgow Looking Glass, November 14, 1825

This caricature depicts the loss of *Fury* to ice, personified by Jack Frost. HMS *Hecla* makes a narrow escape in the background.

North Polar Expedition.

Jack Frost, and the Fury.

27

KNOWLEDGE FROM INUIT

When asked, Inuit often shared detailed information about the Arctic with European explorers, including descriptive names for places, landscape features and travel routes.

Ikmalick and Apelagliu, Nattilingmiut Inuit from the Boothia Peninsula, joined Sir John Ross on *Victory* and added to Ross' chart of the area. Ross published this information, referring to Ikmalick as a hydrographer: a person who describes and maps bodies of water.

INUIT TRADITIONAL KNOWLEDGE

Inuit knowledge of the environment is extensive. Added to over generations, this storehouse of geographical knowledge is shared orally and through representations — maps — created on a variety of permanent and impermanent media.

Carved Wooden Maps — Reproductions
These three-dimensional maps, sometimes referred to as the "Ammassalik Wooden Maps," are an *aide-mémoire* — a tangible navigational aid for a complex area of coastline between the Kangertittivatsiaq and Sermiligaaq Fjords in Tasiilaq, Kalaallit Nunaat (Greenland).

HMS EREBUS AND TERROR

HMS *Erebus* and *Terror* were originally Royal Navy bomb vessels: exceptionally strong ships with large holds able to store great quantities of provisions.

Further strengthened for use in sea ice, their iron-plated bows were reinforced with solid wood up to 8 feet (2.4 metres) thick. A furnace pushed warm air through the lower deck while a new system, using lead pipes, distilled fresh drinking water.

Model of HMS *Erebus*

MODIFICATIONS FOR THE 1845 FRANKLIN EXPEDITION

Erebus and *Terror* underwent additional modifications in 1845, when each was equipped with a 25-horsepower locomotive engine connected to a retractable screw propeller. Each ship carried enough fuel to power the engines for 12 days.

> "To be used only in pushing the ships through channels between masses of ice, when the wind is adverse or calm. But as the supply of fuel is necessarily small, you will use it only in cases of difficulty."
>
> ■ ■ ■
>
> **Admiralty orders to Sir John Franklin**

Plan of Stern Modifications to *Erebus* and *Terror* 1845

THE SENIOR OFFICERS –
CAPTAIN SIR JOHN FRANKLIN

Sir John Franklin commanded the 129-man Expedition — his third attempt to locate a Northwest Passage — and sailed aboard *Erebus*, the Expedition's flagship.

While his overland expedition (1819–1822) was a disaster, costing the lives of 11 men, he was knighted for his more successful 1825–1827 effort.

Smarting from his abrupt recall as Lieutenant-Governor of Van Diemen's Land (Tasmania) in 1843, Franklin believed the 1845 Expedition would redeem his reputation. To that end, he called upon powerful friends to help secure his command.

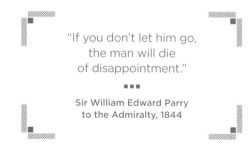

"If you don't let him go, the man will die of disappointment."

■ ■ ■

Sir William Edward Parry
to the Admiralty, 1844

**Daguerreotype Portrait
of Sir John Franklin**

**Sir John Franklin's Naval
General Service Medal**

Copy of a Daguerreotype Portrait
of Captain F. R. M. Crozier

Watch Used by F. R. M. Crozier in the Antarctic
The watch's engraving reads "Presented
by Captain F. R. M. Crozier, R.N., to Sergt
W. K. Cunningham, R.M., as a mark of esteem."

THE SENIOR OFFICERS – CAPTAIN FRANCIS RAWDON MOIRA CROZIER

Francis Crozier was an experienced polar navigator, and second-in-command of the Expedition. He captained *Terror*, which he had also commanded as part of an 1839–1843 expedition to the Antarctic.

Crozier was an expert in terrestrial magnetism, and was elected a Fellow of the Royal Astronomical Society and the Royal Society.

During an earlier Northwest Passage expedition, Crozier interacted frequently with local Inuit, who called him *Aglooka*: "He who takes long strides."

"Captain Crozier was of an amiable and cheerful disposition and his unbending integrity and truthfulness won the affection and respect of those he commanded, as well as the admiration and firm friendship of all those officers under whom he served."

■ ■ ■

Sir James Clark Ross

THE SENIOR OFFICERS – COMMANDER JAMES FITZJAMES

James Fitzjames participated in exploratory and military actions in the Middle East and China before being seriously wounded during the First Opium War (1839–1842).

A favourite of Sir John Barrow, who wanted him in overall command of the Expedition, Fitzjames was its third most senior officer.

Daguerreotype Portrait of Commander James Fitzjames

Royal National Lifeboat Institution Silver Medal and Silver Cup — 1824-1857
Fitzjames was awarded this silver cup and medal, as well as the Freedom of the
City of Liverpool, for rescuing a drowning man from the River Mersey in 1835.

THE FRANKLIN EXPEDITION SETS SAIL

Erebus and *Terror* departed Greenhithe on May 19, 1845.

The last letters and images of the Expedition were sent back with a transport ship, which escorted *Erebus* and *Terror* to the Whale Fish Islands off the west coast of Greenland.

Signal to Terror, Opportunity for Sending Letters
From *Sketches of Captain Owen Stanley* (1845)

June 4. Signal to Terror opportunity
for sending letters to England

HMS **Erebus**
From *Sketches of Captain Owen Stanley* (1845)

LIFE ON BOARD THE SHIPS

Franklin's men benefitted from the experiences of earlier Royal Navy polar expeditions, which had developed routines for passing the cold, dark winter months on ships surrounded by sea ice.

Perilous Position of HMS Terror, *Captain Back, in the Arctic Regions in the Summer of 1837*
Painted by Lieutenant William Smyth, mid-1800s

45

SPACE TO LIVE AND WORK

Space was at a premium on the ships, especially near the beginning of the Expedition when the decks and hold of each were filled with provisions intended to last for at least three years.

The lower deck, a hive of activity, was carefully arranged. Petty Officers, Able Seamen and Royal Marines relaxed, ate and slept around the galley (stove), while officers ate in separate mess rooms and enjoyed private sleeping cabins.

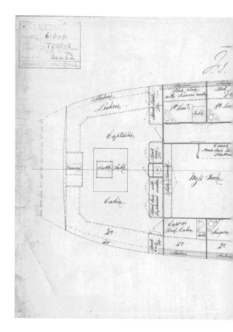

Lower deck plan,
Terror *(1813);* Erebus *(1826)*

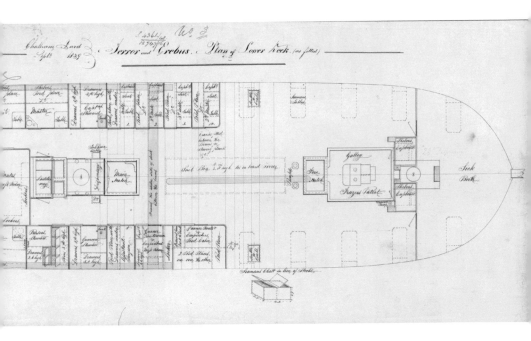

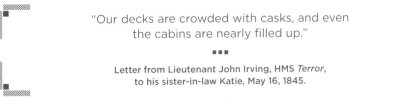

"Our decks are crowded with casks, and even the cabins are nearly filled up."

•••

Letter from Lieutenant John Irving, HMS *Terror*,
to his sister-in-law Katie, May 16, 1845.

"I have now, for instance, at the tables in my cabin, a lieutenant constructing the plan of the survey he has made of the islands of which this group is composed, and Mr. Goodsir, the assistant surgeon and naturalist, with his microscope."

■■■

Letter from Sir John Franklin, HMS *Erebus*, to Sir William Edward Parry, July 10, 1845

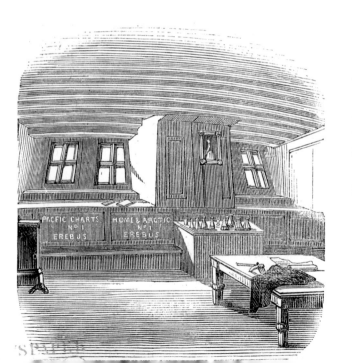

Capt. Sir John Franklin's cabin, in the "Erebus"
The Illustrated London News, May 24, 1845

Capt. [sic] Fitzjames's cabin, in the "Erebus"
The Illustrated London News, May 24, 1845

"I am writing at the little table you will see in
The Illustrated News — only you must imagine that the
table is three feet long, or from the bed to the door."

■ ■ ■

Journal kept by Commander James Fitzjames, HMS *Erebus*

RESEARCH AND SCIENCE

Although Franklin's main task was to chart a Northwest Passage, his Expedition also had a scientific mission.

The Admiralty's instructions included directions for undertaking numerous natural-science pursuits.

The importance of this work was clear to Commander Fitzjames, who noted "the necessity of observing everything from a flea to a whale in the unknown regions we are to visit."

On Several New Species of Crustaceans Allied to Saphirina
The Expedition produced a single scientific paper, sent to Britain from Greenland for publication by Dr. Harry Goodsir. Goodsir, Acting Assistant Surgeon on *Erebus*, was also the Expedition's naturalist.

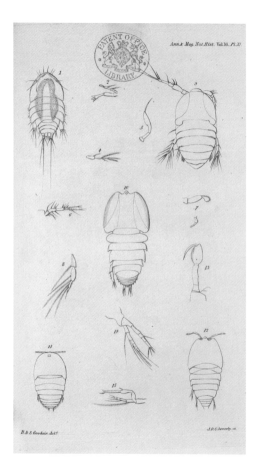

SHIP LIBRARIES

Erebus and *Terror* were equipped with libraries containing a variety of religious, scientific and leisure books, as well as the written accounts of earlier polar explorers.

"I've got here a catalogue of all the books, public and private there are on board (and the *Terror* is doing the same) and we find there is scarcely a book that we can think of as being required that is not in the list. We shall supply each other with these lists, and thus, when a book is wanted, the Librarian (Goodsir) will at once know which ship and what cabin it is in."

■■■

Letter from Lieutenant James Fairholme, HMS *Erebus*, to his father, July 1, 1845

LEISURE ACTIVITIES

Free time was part of shipboard life, allowing everyone to engage in various forms of leisure. Card and board games were played, and men might dance or exercise to a crewmate's musical instrument, or one of 50 songs played on their ship's hand-organ.

During the winter months, officers and crew were required to spend time outdoors, where they could play cricket and soccer, or go for a walk.

"I have just had a game of chess with Osmer, who is delightful, always good humoured, always laughing, never a bore, plays a 'rubber' [a score in the card game bridge] and beats me at chess."

■■■

Journal kept by Commander James Fitzjames, HMS *Erebus*

Arctic amusements
Dec.N. 1836. O.S.

The Drawings Made by Captain Owen Stanley When on the Arctic Expedition Commanded by Sir George Back in HMS "Terror" 1836 and 1837

ARCTIC AMUSEMENTS

This scene shows a night of musical theatre aboard *Terror* in 1836. Such evenings were a favourite pastime, with officers and men participating in performances during the long months of winter confinement.

> "At present, Saturday night seems to be kept up in due nautical form around my cabin, a fiddle going on as hard as it can and 2 or 3 different songs from the forecastle [the sailor's living quarters]. In short, all seems quite happy."
>
> ■■■
>
> **Letter from Lieutenant James Fairholme, HMS *Erebus*, to his father, May 17, 1845**

THE CAMP AT CAPE FELIX, KING WILLIAM ISLAND

Northwest Passage expeditions were rarely idle, especially in spring when the sun returned. Lieutenant Irving of *Terror* wrote of a plan to send "exploring parties out on foot while the ships are frozen in."

The Expedition established a camp at Cape Felix on King William Island. Although its purpose is unclear, the camp likely involved 10 to 12 men who built a stone cairn and lived in three tents.

COOKING APPARATUS.

(1)

PORTABLE COOKING APPARATUS FOUND ON THE N.W. SHORE KING WILLIAM ISLAND.

Portable Cooking Stove
A large variety of materials was left at Cape Felix, including this portable cooking stove, which was probably made aboard *Erebus* or *Terror* for use by travelling parties.

LEAVING A TRAIL OF MESSAGES

The Expedition was instructed to throw notes overboard, sealed in metal cannisters, once the ships passed 65° N. Finders were requested, in six languages, to forward records to the Admiralty.

The Expedition was supplied with 200 canisters.

Message Canister
This canister contained the record left by the Franklin Expedition in 1847, at Victory Point on King William Island. The canister was retrieved and its record updated in 1848.

TUNUNIQ – THE BACK OF BEYOND

Franklin's ships became beset off the northwest coast of King William Island, in a region known as Tununiq (also written as Toonoonee). Inuit rarely visited the region in the mid-1800s, associating it with unrelenting cold, poor hunting and starvation.

The region remains a harsh place. Even with today's reduced ice coverage, this is often the last part of the Northwest Passage to clear.

In some years, the ice does not leave at all.

"The coast from Point Victory northward was heavy close pack, consisting of all descriptions of ice, but for the most part old and heavy."

■■■

Francis Leopold McClintock,
The Voyage of the "Fox" in the Arctic Seas, 1859

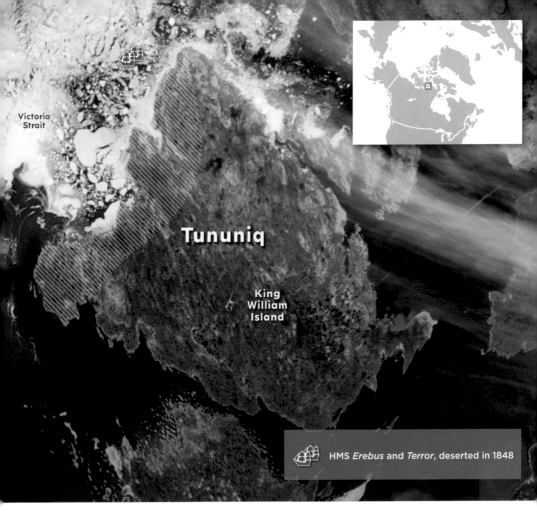

Victoria
Strait

Tununiq

King
William
Island

HMS *Erebus* and *Terror*, deserted in 1848

THE

SEARCH FOR

FRANKLIN

Northwest Passage expeditions fuelled the public's fascination with the Arctic. The published accounts of those voyages, filled with descriptions of ice and exotic people and animals, turned polar explorers — especially those who had survived adversity — into household names.

John Franklin — "the man who ate his boots" during his disastrous 1819–1822 Northwest Passage expedition — became a national hero.

Staffordshire Figurines of Sir John and Lady Jane Franklin
Early 1850s

INUIT IN EUROPE

Europeans had a long history of bringing Inuit to Europe, first as proof of their exploits and later as curiosities. Almost all Inuit were unwilling participants, and virtually all died before they returned home.

This pattern continued through the 1800s, as entire families were brought to Europe. Most were exhibited in "ethnological expositions" — human zoos — which were hugely popular shows that often toured for years.

Mikak and Her Son Tukauk
Painted by John Russell, 1769

Mikak was a Labrador Inuit woman taken to Britain in 1767. Her portrait was commissioned by Sir Joseph Banks, for whom Banks Island in the Arctic is named. Mikak and Tukauk returned to Labrador in 1769.

LADY JANE FRANKLIN AND THE MISSING EXPEDITION

When 1847 brought no news of the Expedition, Lady Franklin began a letter-writing campaign, entreating officials to find her husband and his men.

THE SEARCH FOR THE FRANKLIN EXPEDITION

More than 30 expeditions, organized or supported by the Royal Navy, the Hudson's Bay Company and private sponsors, sailed, steamed or sledged into the Arctic from 1847 onwards.

Very few found any clues to the Expedition's whereabouts.

"My anxiety for the fate of my long-absent husband, and of his companions, forbids me to leave any means untried on their behalf."

■ ■ ■

Letter from Lady Jane Franklin to the Lords of the Admiralty, December 11, 1849

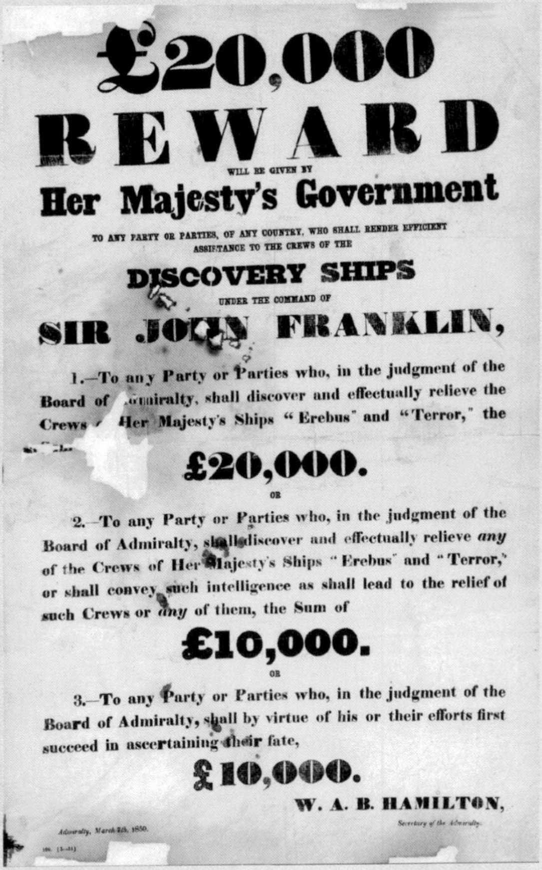

£20,000 REWARD

WILL BE GIVEN BY

Her Majesty's Government

TO ANY PARTY OR PARTIES, OF ANY COUNTRY, WHO SHALL RENDER EFFICIENT ASSISTANCE TO THE CREWS OF THE

DISCOVERY SHIPS

UNDER THE COMMAND OF

SIR JOHN FRANKLIN,

1.—To any Party or Parties who, in the judgment of the Board of [illegible]miralty, shall discover and effectually relieve the Crews [illegible] Her Majesty's Ships "Erebus" and "Terror," the [illegible]

£20,000.

OR

2.—To any Party or Parties who, in the judgment of the Board of Admiralty, shall discover and effectually relieve *any* of the Crews of Her Majesty's Ships "Erebus" and "Terror," or shall convey such intelligence as shall lead to the relief of such Crews or *any* of them, the Sum of

£10,000.

OR

3.—To any Party or Parties who, in the judgment of the Board of Admiralty, shall by virtue of his or their efforts first succeed in ascertaining their fate,

£10,000.

W. A. B. HAMILTON,

Secretary of the Admiralty.

Admiralty, March 7th, 1850.

£20,000 Reward for the Discovery of the Franklin Expedition
March 7, 1850

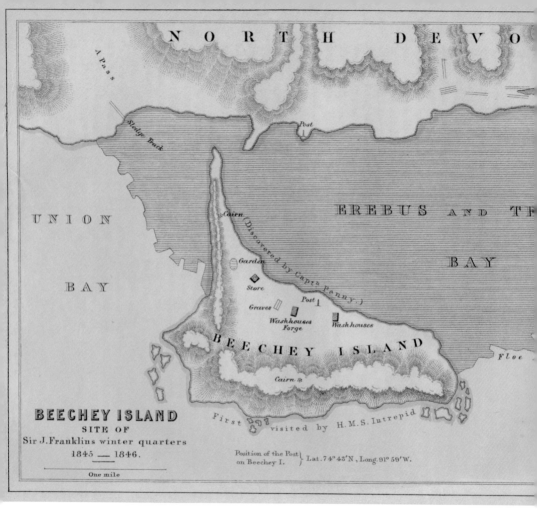

BEECHEY ISLAND
SITE OF
Sir J. Franklins winter quarters
1845 — 1846.

One mile

Position of the Post } Lat. 74° 43′ N., Long. 91° 59′ W.
on Beechey I.

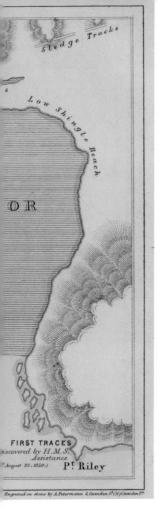

Beechey Island, Sir J. Franklin's Winter Quarters
From Papers and Despatches Relating to the Arctic
Searching Expeditions of 1850-51-52 (1852)

BEECHEY ISLAND

The first traces of the Expedition were found in 1850 on the sheltered inner shore of Beechey Island, where the Expedition's main 1845–1846 overwintering camp had been located.

But the Expedition left no discernable clue to its route, once it departed. Franklin had again disappeared.

THE BELCHER SEARCH EXPEDITION, 1852–1854

The Royal Navy's final — and largest — Franklin search expedition was commanded by Sir Edward Belcher. His ships assembled at Beechey Island, before two vessels were sent west to Melville Island. Belcher took two other ships north into Wellington Channel, while a fifth stayed at Beechey Island.

No new traces of the Franklin Expedition were found.

RESCUING THE RESCUERS

The crews of HMS *Resolute* and HMS *Intrepid*, part of the Belcher expedition, established a large storehouse on Dealy Island, off Melville Island, in 1853.

Although they found no trace of Franklin, they did locate HMS *Investigator*, another Franklin search vessel trapped by ice in Mercy Bay on the northern coast of Banks Island.

Man-Hauled Sledge
This sledge, left on Melville Island, was part of the equipment supplied to *Resolute* and *Intrepid*. It may be the sledge, used between April and July 1853, that Francis Leopold McClintock called "Star of the North."

INUIT SALVAGE OF SEARCHERS' SUPPLIES

Before *Investigator* was abandoned, tons of its supplies were cached ashore, becoming a valuable resource for Inuinnait ("Copper Inuit").

Investigator's wood and metal have been found in many archaeological sites on Banks Island, revealing how Inuinnait adapted this material for their own uses.

Message Tin and Fragmentary Notes
Cornwallis Island

The papers inside this message canister, a repurposed ammunition box, were damaged when the container was bitten by a polar bear.

MAINTAINING COMMUNICATION

Parties searching for the Franklin Expedition tried to stay in touch with one another — a difficult task, given the enormity of the search area.

Messages were usually written on paper and stashed inside metal canisters. They typically included the date of their deposition, the whereabouts of search vessels, and the location of cached provisions.

Message Stamped Into a Lead Plaque
Northumberland Sound, Devon Island

The lead plaque bears a message, made aboard HMS *Assistance*, giving the date and quantity of provisions that were cached.

INUIT REVEAL THE EXPEDITION'S FATE

Dr. John Rae was an accomplished Arctic traveller who worked closely with Indigenous groups. He heard the first details of the Expedition's fate in 1854 from Inuit who spoke of seeing starving and dead Europeans.

Rae purchased Franklin's Guelphic Order and other Expedition objects from the Inuit, and sent a report to Britain. Although Rae had not intended this report, which included details of cannibalism, to be made public, it was published by the Admiralty.

Rae, and the Inuit, were vilified.

Sir John Franklin's Royal Guelphic Order
Sir John Franklin was made a Knight Commander of the Royal Guelphic Order on January 25, 1836. He is wearing the Order in his 1845 daguerreotype portrait.

THE ADMIRALTY ENDS ITS SEARCH FOR FRANKLIN

Franklin's Expedition, equipped to last three years, was missing for more than eight when the Admiralty announced that its officers and men would be declared dead as of March 31, 1854.

Notice Respecting the Officers and Crews of Her Majesty's Ships *Erebus* and *Terror*
London Gazette, January 20, 1854

NARROWING THE SEARCH

Lady Franklin, although repelled by Rae's report, believed that the area identified by the Inuit needed to be examined. When the Admiralty refused to arrange additional searches, Lady Franklin planned and largely funded another effort, enlisting Francis Leopold McClintock.

Lady Jane Franklin
Chalk on paper sketch by Thomas Bock, 1838

FRANCIS LEOPOLD McCLINTOCK

McClintock headed for the Arctic in 1857. Sledging down the west coast of the Boothia Peninsula, McClintock met Inuit who had Expedition materials and additional information on the Franklin ships and their crews.

Circling King William Island in 1859, McClintock's party located several Franklin Expedition sites, including Crozier's Landing, the Expedition's landfall after deserting *Erebus* and *Terror* in 1848.

Shotgun Left Beside a Ship's Boat at Crozier's Landing

Transcript of the Victory Point Note

28 of May 1847

H.M.S.hips Erebus and Terror Wintered in the Ice in Lat. 70°5'N Long. 98°23'W Having wintered in 1846-7 [*sic*] at Beechey Island in Lat 74°43'28"N Long 91°39'15"W

After having ascended Wellington Channel to Lat 77° and returned by the West side of Cornwallis Island.

Sir John Franklin commanding the Expedition.

<u>All well</u>

Party consisting of 2 Officers and 6 Men left the ships on Monday 24th May 1847.

[signed] Gm. Gore, Lieut.

[signed] Chas. F. DesVoeux, Mate

25th April 1848

HMShips Terror and Erebus were deserted on the 22nd April 5 leagues NNW of this having been beset since 12th Sept 1846.

The officers and crews consisting of 105 souls under the command of Captain F. R. M. Crozier landed here — in Lat. 69°37'42" Long. 98°41'

This paper was found by Lt. Irving under the cairn supposed to have been built by Sir James Ross in 1831 — 4 miles to the Northward — where it had been deposited by the late Commander Gore in May June 1847.

Sir James Ross' pillar has not however been found and the paper has been transferred to this position which is that in which Sir J. Ross' pillar was erected.

Sir John Franklin died on the 11th of June 1847 and the total loss by deaths in the Expedition has been to this date 9 officers and 15 men.

[signed] F. R. M. Crozier Captain & Senior Offr

And start on tomorrow 26th for Backs Fish River

[signed] James Fitzjames Captain HMS Erebus

VICTORY POINT NOTE

The Victory Point Note consists of two very different messages. The earlier, dated May 1847, ends "All well" and does not suggest any major calamities.

The April 1848 message, written around the record's margin, is very different. It reports the deaths of Sir John Franklin and approximately 20 per cent of the Expedition crew, as well as the desertion of *Erebus* and *Terror*.

This communication has been the foundation for many competing interpretations of the Expedition's end.

Masonic Seal
The device on this glass seal, found inside an abandoned boat in Erebus Bay, features a builder's square and compass, symbols of Freemasonry. We do not know who among Franklin's men was a Mason, but notable past members have included Winston Churchill, John Diefenbaker and George Washington.

Sledge Harness From *Terror*
Collected by Schwatka at Crozier's
Landing on King William Island

CHARLES FRANCIS HALL AND FREDERICK SCHWATKA

The final two major Franklin searches of the 1800s were overland expeditions that employed Inuit guides and interpreters and lived largely off the land.

Charles Francis Hall, with Taqulittuq and Ipivik, interviewed Inuit witnesses and, between 1865 and 1869, compiled an invaluable record of the Expedition's final days.

Frederick Schwatka travelled to the western coast of King William Island in 1878 and 1879, collecting additional Franklin materials and noting burial sites in Erebus Bay.

PART OF A BLOCK
FROM
N.W. PASSAGE.

Block Sheave (Top) and Fragment of Boat Mast (Bottom)
Collected by Schwatka at Wilmot and Crampton Bay, Adelaide Peninsula

TRAVEL OVER LAND

The Franklin Expedition was instructed to complete a Northwest Passage by ship.

Although some sledging was anticipated while *Erebus* and *Terror* were immobilized by sea ice, the Expedition's crew was ill-equipped for longer-term land-based travel.

Improvised Crampon
Screws have been driven through the leather sole of this shoe to give its wearer better traction on ice and snow. It was collected at Crozier's Landing, the Expedition's landfall after its ships were deserted in April 1848.

BAD LUCK, BAD TIMING, BAD ICE

Although the details may never be fully known, ice ultimately destroyed the Franklin Expedition.

When Franklin's ships entered Victoria Strait, they confronted some of the worst conditions imaginable. The heavy ice streaming into Victoria Strait piles against King William Island, creating one of the most severe ice-choke points in the Arctic.

No matter how strong or well prepared *Erebus* and *Terror* were, once they were trapped, they were at the ice's mercy.

Belaying Pins
Recovered from *Erebus*, September 2015

Rigging ropes are fastened (belayed) to a ship's upper deck by wrapping them around belaying pins inserted through pinrails near the masts and ship's sides. Two of these solid metal belaying pins were bent or broken when great force — likely from ice — was exerted on them, probably when *Erebus*' rigging collapsed.

DEATH IN THE ICE

The Victory Point Note records that 24 crewmembers were already dead when HMS *Erebus* and *Terror* were deserted in April 1848.

Even if the remaining 105 men survived, the Franklin Expedition would still have had the highest death rate of any Royal Navy Northwest Passage expedition. The question remains: why?

Skulls of Members of the Franklin Expedition Discovered and Buried by William Skinner and Paddy Gibson on King William Island
Unknown photographer, around 1931

THE THREE GRAVES ON BEECHEY ISLAND

Three members of the Franklin Expedition died and were buried on Beechey Island, where the ships spent the winter of 1845–1846.

The men's relatively well-preserved remains were exhumed and autopsied in 1984 and 1986. Ongoing analyses of hair, bone and nail samples have identified several possible causes of death.

John Torrington, Leading Stoker on *Terror*, became the Expedition's first casualty when he died on January 1, 1846. He was only 20 years of age.

John Hartnell, an Able Seaman on *Erebus*, was in his mid-20s when he died three days later. He was autopsied before his burial, suggesting that there was some concern regarding his cause of death.

William Braine, a Royal Marine on *Erebus*, died at the beginning of April. Like Torrington and Hartnell, he suffered from tuberculosis.

The Graves of Three of Franklin's Crewmen on Beechey Island
By J. Hamilton, after a sketch by Elisha Kent Kane

WHAT KILLED THE MEN OF THE FRANKLIN EXPEDITION?

Injuries and illnesses would have been recorded in the Sick Books of *Erebus* and *Terror*. Without these records, researchers can only speculate about the health issues experienced in the years after the Expedition left Britain.

SCURVY

Scurvy is caused by a lack of vitamin C, which is found in citrus fruits, uncooked meat, and some fresh vegetables. From 1795, the Royal Navy prescribed lemon juice, which is rich in vitamin C, eliminating most instances of ship-board scurvy.

Symptoms include tiredness, irritability and malaise, joint pain, easy bruising, inflamed and bleeding gums, tooth loss, and weight loss. In addition, old wounds may reopen.

Inuit described meeting Franklin crewmembers with blackened mouths, a clear symptom of scurvy.

"They forged the last link with their lives": Sir John Franklin's men dying by their boat during the North-West Passage expedition Painted by William Thomas Smith, 1895

EVERYDAY HEALTH ISSUES

Any number of normally manageable health conditions and otherwise survivable injuries would become increasingly dangerous as conditions worsened on the Expedition.

One crewmember buried within the Franklin Memorial outside the Chapel of the Old Royal Naval College at Greenwich — possibly Dr. Harry Goodsir, Acting Surgeon on *Erebus* — had a periapical void (dental abscess).

What began as a simple toothache became an infection that may have ultimately led to his death.

Franklin Memorial
Old Royal Naval College, Greenwich

TUBERCULOSIS

Tuberculosis is an infectious bacterial disease affecting the lungs and, more rarely, the bones.

Tuberculosis was commonly called "consumption," due to the marked weight loss it caused. All three men buried on Beechey Island were emaciated and suffered from tuberculosis.

LEAD POISONING

Lead is a heavy metal absorbed through the skin and digestive system. Continued exposure may cause lead toxicity.

Lead poisoning can result in a number of behavioural changes, including mental confusion and memory loss.

Some Expedition crewmembers had very high levels of lead, probably from lead-soldered food tins and the ships' freshwater drinking system. The effect of lead on the Expedition's overall health continues to be debated.

SURVIVAL CANNIBALISM

Inuit witnesses spoke of cannibalism among members of the Franklin Expedition. Forensic studies clearly support these accounts.

About 25 per cent of the human bones found in Erebus Bay exhibit the types of cut marks associated with butchery and dismemberment. There are also indications that some bones were cracked open and boiled to extract their calorie-rich marrow, confirming Inuit reports of human bones "broken up for the marrow" and left "close to the cooking place."

"From the mutilated state of many of the corpses and the contents of the kettles, it is evident that our wretched countrymen had been driven to the last dread resource — cannibalism — as a means of prolonging existence."

■■■

From the report of John Rae to the Admiralty, July 29, 1854

"Outside the boat he saw a number of skulls. He forgot how many, but said there were more than four. He also saw bones from legs and arms that appeared to have been sawed off. Inside the boat was a box filled with bones. The appearance of the bones led the Inuit to the opinion that the white men had been eating each other."

■■■

Testimony provided by Tooktoocheer to Frederick Schwatka, in W. H. Gilder, *Schwatka's Search: Sledging in the Arctic in Quest of the Franklin Records,* 1882

IDENTIFYING MEMBERS OF THE FRANKLIN EXPEDITION

The Government of Nunavut has been leading the land-based component of the Franklin Expedition investigation since 2008.

Working at archaeological sites around King William Island, Dr. Douglas Stenton has collected skeletal remains of Franklin Expedition crewmembers for analysis.

DNA samples have been taken in an effort to identify individual crewmembers. If you are a genetic descendant of a member of the Franklin Expedition, you can submit your DNA to help in this identification process by contacting Dr. Stenton.

Dr. Stenton Excavating Human Remains
Erebus Bay, King William Island

FRANKLIN'S SHIPS FOUND!

⸻ ❖ ⸻

Inuit oral histories preserve details of the ship discovered at Utjulik, an area west of the Adelaide Peninsula which includes Wilmot and Crampton Bay. This ship was visited repeatedly by Inuit, who removed useful items, later adapted into tools, until the ship sank in shallow water. Its masts, visible for a time, were eventually torn away by sea ice.

"On getting aboard [the Inuit] tried to find out if [anyone] was there. To get into the igloo (cabin), they knocked a hole through because it was locked ... one place on the ship, where a great many things were found, was very dark; they had to find things there by feeling around ... there was meat and *tood-noo* in cans, the meat fat and like pemmican. The sails, rigging, and boats — everything about the ship — was in complete order. [After some time the Inuit] found her sunk, except the top of the masts ... The ship was afterward much broken up by the ice, and then masts, timbers, boxes, casks, &c., drifted on shore."

■■■

The Utjulik ship, as described to Charles Francis Hall by Inukpuhiijuk (In-nook-poo-zhee-jook)

A SUCCESSFUL SEARCH

Under the leadership of Parks Canada, a renewed search for Franklin's ships began in 2008. The search involved a number of public and private partners.

Multiple teams worked together to survey the coastline and waters of King William Island and the Adelaide Peninsula, including where *Erebus* and *Terror* were deserted and where Inuit accounts indicated they sank.

CCGS *Sir Wilfrid Laurier* Navigating Through Sea Ice

Dr. Stenton, a Government of Nunavut Archaeologist, Documenting the Davit Pintle

Davit Pintle

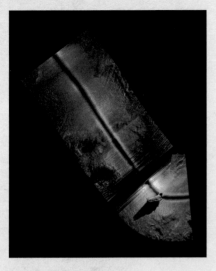

Sonar Image of *Erebus*
A sonar image of *Erebus*, visible on the lower right, taken on September 2, 2014, the day of its discovery.

A SHIP'S DAVIT PINTLE

An important clue was found on September 1, 2014, on an island in Wilmot and Crampton Bay. Andrew Stirling, a Transport Canada helicopter pilot working with Government of Nunavut archaeologists, found an iron davit pintle (fitting) behind a rock, where it had lain for generations.

Parks Canada, already conducting a sonar search of the nearby ocean floor, quickly refocused its efforts near that island.

Erebus was found the next day.

"That's it! That's it!"

■ ■ ■

Ryan Harris, Senior Underwater Archaeologist with Parks Canada

IDENTIFYING EREBUS

Erebus was pinpointed and recorded using different types of sonar equipment. By comparing these and other images from a remotely operated vehicle against ship plans held at the National Maritime Museum, Parks Canada researchers not only confirmed the discovery of a three-masted wooden ship, but its identity as Franklin's flagship — *Erebus*.

Parks Canada Underwater Archaeology Team
Studying Sonar Images and Ship Plans

FINDING TERROR

Unbelievably, almost two years to the day after the discovery of *Erebus*, *Terror* was located in Terror Bay, off the southern coast of King William Island.

Found using information provided by Sammy Kogvik, an Inuk from Gjoa Haven, *Terror* is in deeper water than *Erebus* and is even better preserved.

Ship's Wheel, HMS *Terror*

FOOTPRINTS

Recovered from the lower deck of *Erebus* near the officer's cabins, this boot fitted the left foot and had seal fur inserted for additional warmth.

Inukpuhiijuk told Charles Francis Hall about the footprints of three or four men, and a dog's paw prints, seen in the snow on the Adelaide Peninsula.

Those footprints may have been left by the last survivors of the Expedition, as they walked away from *Erebus* for the final time.

Officer's Leather Boot
Recovered from *Erebus*, September 2015

A MISSING BLADE

This elaborate sword hilt, found near the officers' cabins on *Erebus*, has a pommel shaped like a lion's head. The sword's steel blade is missing, although what happened to it is unclear.

Francis Leopold McClintock purchased a number of Expedition materials from Inuit in 1859. They told him that the blade of one knife had been broken from a piece that was originally "as long as his arm." Were they referring to a sword?

Sword Hilt
Recovered from *Erebus*, September 2015

THE EREBUS BELL

The ship's bell was the first artifact recovered from *Erebus*. It is marked with a broad arrow — indicating it is British government property — and "1845," the year Franklin's Expedition departed Britain.

Ship's Bell
As discovered on *Erebus*, September 2014 (left) and after conservation (right)

BLUE WILLOW CERAMIC PLATES

The Royal Navy introduced mass-produced round plates during the 1840s, replacing earlier square wooden trays, from which the expression "a square meal" may originate.

Lower-ranking members of the Expedition would have used plates like these every day.

Blue Willow Ceramic Plates
After conservation (left); a Parks Canada archaeologist records the position of the plates on the lower deck of *Erebus* (right)

MANY QUESTIONS REMAIN

The discovery of *Erebus* and *Terror* was international news — the thrilling culmination of more than 165 years of searching.

But their locations, far south of where they were first deserted in April 1848, raise new questions. Did the vessels escape the ice only to drift aimlessly to their final locations, or were they guided? Why did so many men die in Erebus Bay? Will researchers find the Expedition's records intact?

Answers to these questions are potentially years away.

Franklin Expedition Route 1846–1848 (probable)

HMS *Erebus* and *Terror*, deserted in 1848

Beechey Island

Boothia Peninsula

Victoria Island

Victoria Strait

Cambridge Bay

Northern Search Area

King William Island

Terror Wreck Site

Gjoa Haven

Queen Maud Gulf

Erebus Wreck Site

Southern Search Area

km
0   25   50   75   100

WRECKS OF HMS EREBUS AND HMS TERROR NATIONAL HISTORIC SITE OF CANADA

This is the first jointly managed National Historic Site of Canada in Nunavut. Reflecting the critical role played by Inuit in their discovery, Nunavummiut (people of Nunavut) and Parks Canada will work together to preserve and protect the wrecks.

Youths in Cambridge Bay Examining a Replica of the *Erebus* Bell

REMEMBERING THE MEN OF THE FRANKLIN EXPEDITION

Lady Franklin erected a memorial to her husband in the Chapel of St. John the Evangelist, at Westminster Abbey. Alfred, Lord Tennyson, Sir John Franklin's nephew, composed a verse that is engraved on the memorial.

THE MISSING MEN

The Franklin Expedition left Britain on May 19, 1845. By April 22, 1848, when HMS *Erebus* and *Terror* were first deserted off the northwest coast of King William Island, 24 crewmembers had died. The remainder appear to have perished on or near King William Island.

The skeletal remains of two Expedition members — Lieutenant John Irving (*Terror*) and possibly Dr. Harry Goodsir (*Erebus*) — were returned to Britain. They, along with the three men interred on Beechey Island, are the only men whose burial sites are currently known.

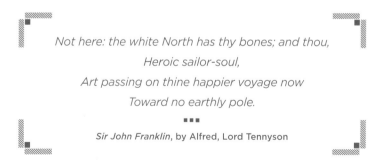

Not here: the white North has thy bones; and thou,

Heroic sailor-soul,

Art passing on thine happier voyage now

Toward no earthly pole.

■■■

Sir John Franklin, by Alfred, Lord Tennyson

LIEUTENANT JAMES W. FAIRHOLME, HMS EREBUS

James Fairholme was selected for the Franklin Expedition by Commander James Fitzjames, with whom Fairholme had served during an 1839 conflict in Syria.

Fitzjames considered Fairholme "a smart, agreeable companion, and a well-informed man."

"I hope Elizabeth [James' sister] got my photograph. Lady Franklin said she thought it made me look too old, but as I had Fitzjames' coat on at the time, to save myself the trouble of getting my own, you will perceive that I am a Commander! and have anchors on the epaulettes so it will do capitally when that really is the case."

■■■

Letter from Lieutenant James W. Fairholme, HMS *Erebus*, to his father, May 29, 1845

Salt Print of Fairholme's Daguerreotype Portrait

TRACES
by H.M.S.
Assistance
1850.) Pt Riley

e Beach

THE ARCTIC MEDAL

The Arctic Medal was the first British medal issued for Arctic service. It was awarded to military and civilian recipients who searched for a Northwest Passage, or traces of the Franklin Expedition, between 1818 and 1855.

Arctic Medal, 1818–1855
Awarded posthumously to Lieutenant Fairholme

THE LIEUTENANT JAMES W. FAIRHOLME COLLECTION

The descendants of those who died on the Franklin Expedition retain their connections with the Expedition and the Royal Navy's long history of polar exploration.

The Canadian Museum of History recently acquired a collection of artifacts, carefully handed down through Lieutenant Fairholme's family, which serve as a memorial to his life.

Dessert Fork, Arctic Medal and Case
From Lieutenant Fairholme's collection

JAMES REID, ICE MASTER, HMS EREBUS

James Reid was a Scottish whaling captain. He was selected for the Expedition because of his experience in the ice-covered waters of Baffin Bay.

James Fitzjames described him as being "as merry-hearted as any young man, always good humoured, beats me at chess — and, he is a gentleman."

Daguerreotype Portrait of James Reid

AN ENGRAVED TIMEPIECE

John Rae purchased this timepiece, engraved "James Reid," from Inuit who found it in a camp northwest of the Back River, where a large group of Expedition crewmen had succumbed to starvation.

"You must not trouble your mind about me. If I always knew you were well, I would be happier. What is to become of my three dear young ones if anything is the matter with you? But I trust the Lord will spare you all so that I may enjoy you for a number of years."

■■■

Letter from James Reid, Ice Master, HMS *Erebus*, to his wife, July 11, 1845

Gold Watch Dust Cover

LIEUTENANT GRAHAM GORE, HMS EREBUS

Graham Gore first participated in the search for a Northwest Passage during George Back's near-disastrous 1836–1837 voyage with HMS *Terror*.

Gore led a sledge party to King William Island in May 1847, depositing the record at Victory Point. The April 1848 addition to the Victory Point Note referred to Gore as "the late Commander," indicating that he had been promoted but had also died in the intervening 11 months.

"Graham Gore, the first lieutenant, a man of great stability of character, a very good officer, and the sweetest of tempers. He plays the flute dreadfully well, draws sometimes very well, sometimes very badly, but is altogether a capital fellow."

■ ■ ■

Journal kept by Commander James Fitzjames, HMS *Erebus*

Daguerreotype Portrait of Graham Gore

A Manual of Private Devotions
"G. Back to Graham Gore May 1845" is inscribed inside this book, indicating that Gore and his old commander had been in contact prior to the Franklin Expedition's May 1845 departure.

THE CREW

HMS EREBUS Name (age, if recorded)		HMS TERROR Name (age, if recorded)
OFFICERS		
Sir John Franklin (59)	Captain	Francis R. M. Crozier (49)
James Fitzjames	Commander	
Graham Gore Henry T. D. Le Vesconte James W. Fairholme	Lieutenants	Edward Little George H. Hodgson John Irving
Robert O. Sargent Charles F. Des Voeux Edward Couch	Mates	Frederick Hornby Robert Thomas
Henry F. Collins	Second Master	Gillies A. Macbean
Stephen S. Stanley	Surgeon	
	Surgeon (Acting)	John S. Peddie
	Assistant Surgeon	Alexander Macdonald
Harry D. S. Goodsir	Assistant Surgeon (Acting)	
Charles H. Osmer	Paymaster and Purser	
	Clerk in Charge	Edwin J. H. Helpman
James Reid	Acting Master (Ice Master)	Thomas Blanky
WARRANT OFFICERS		
Thomas Terry	Boatswain	John Lane
John Weekes	Carpenter	Thomas Honey
John Gregory	Engineer	James Thompson

PETTY OFFICERS

Samuel Brown (27)	Boatswain's Mate	Thomas Johnson (28)
Thomas Watson (40)	Carpenter's Mate	Alexander Wilson (27)
Philip Reddington (28)	Captain of the Forecastle	Reuben Male (27)
Daniel Arthur (35) William Bell (36) John Downing (34)	Quartermasters	David McDonald (46) John Kenley (44) William Rhodes (31)
John Murray (43)	Sailmaker	
James W. Brown (28)	Caulker	Thomas Darlington (29)
William Smith (25)	Blacksmith	Samuel Honey (22)
James Hart (33)	Leading Stoker	John Torrington (19)
Richard Wall (45)	Ship's Cook	John Diggle (36)
James Rigden (32)	Captain's Coxswain	John Wilson (33)
John Sullivan (28)	Captain of the Maintop	Thomas R. Farr (32)
Robert Sinclair (25)	Captain of the Foretop	Henry Peglar (37)
Joseph Andrews (35)	Captain of the Hold	William Goddard (39)
Francis Dunn (25)	Caulker's Mate	Cornelius Hickey (24)
Edmund Hoar (23)	Captain's Steward	Thomas Jopson (27)
Richard Aylmore (24)	Gunroom Steward	Thomas Armitage (40)
William Fowler (26)	Paymaster and Purser's Steward	Edward Genge (21)
John Bridgens (26)	Subordinate Officers' Steward	William Gibson (22)
John Cowie (32) Thomas Plater	Stokers	William Johnson (45) Luke Smith (27)

ABLE SEAMEN

Charles Best (23) | William Clossan (25)
Charles Coombs (28) | Robert Ferrier (29)
Josephus Geater (32) | John Hartnell (25)
Thomas Hartnell (23) | Robert Johns (24)
Henry Lloyd (26) | William Mark (24)
Thomas McConvey (24) | John Morfin (25)
William Orren (34) | Francis Pocock (24)
Abraham Seely (34) | John Stickland (24)
Thomas Tadman (28) | George Thompson (27)
George Williams (35) | Thomas Work (41)

John Bailey (21) | John Bates (24)
Alexander Berry (32) | George J. Cann (23)
Samuel Crispe (24) | John Handford (28)
William Jerry (29) | Charles Johnson (28)
George Kinnaird (23) | Edwin Lawrence (30)
David Leys (37) | Magnus Manson (28)
Henry Sait (23) | William Shanks (29)
David Sims (24) | William Sinclair (30)
William Strong (22) | James Walker (29)
William Wentzall (33)

ROYAL MARINES

Daniel Bryant (31)	Sergeant	Solomon Tozer (34)
Alexander Paterson (30)	Corporal	William Hedges (30)
William Braine (31) Joseph Healey (29) Robert Hopcraft (38) William Pilkington (28) William Reed (28)	Privates	James Daly (30) John Hammond (32) William Heather (35) Henry Wilks (28)

BOYS

George Chambers (18) David Young (18)	Thomas Evans (18) Robert Golding (19)

CONTRIBUTIONS

An exhibition and catalogue on the Franklin Expedition would not have been possible without Claire Champ, Danielle Goyer and Kerry McMaster, as well as Canadian Museum of History staff working in Collections Management and Conservation, Project Management and Technical Services, Scenography and Media Production, and Business Partnerships and Information Management. Their hard work and dedication are greatly appreciated. At Parks Canada, Meryl Oliver, Johanne Ranger, Tamara Tarasoff and the Underwater Archaeology Team headed by Marc-André Bernier deserve special mention, as do the National Maritime Museum's Sandra Adler, Céline Dalcher and Helen Schulte. It was a pleasure to work with Eva Aariak, William Beveridge and Ralph Kownak at the Inuit Heritage Trust, as well as Douglas Stenton (Government of Nunavut).

This catalogue was shepherded by Lee Wyndham, and InnovaCom Marketing & Communication pulled everything together.

PHOTO CREDITS

p. 63   Library and Archives Canada, e010754422

p. 64   A. Petermann, Library and Archives Canada, e011183612

p. 66   © National Maritime Museum, Greenwich, London, AAA2026

p. 69   CMH IMG2016-0321-0016-Dm, Steven Darby

p. 71   CMH IMG2016-0321-0022-Dm, Steven Darby

p. 72   *(top)* CMH IMG2016-0321-0013-Dm, Steven Darby

p. 72   *(bottom)* CMH IMG2016-0321-0036-Dm, Steven Darby

p. 74   © National Maritime Museum, Greenwich, London, AAA2079

p. 75   The National Archives, ZJ 1/283

p. 76   Collection of Queen Victoria Museum & Art Gallery, Launceston, Australia

p. 77   © National Maritime Museum, Greenwich, London, AAA2531

p. 78   © National Maritime Museum, Greenwich, London, HSR/C/9/1

p. 79   © National Maritime Museum, Greenwich, London, AAA2197

p. 80   © National Maritime Museum, Greenwich, London, AAA2261

p. 81   © National Maritime Museum, Greenwich, London, AAA2276

p. 82   © National Maritime Museum, Greenwich, London, AAA2299 and AAA2300

p. 83   CMH IMG2016-0321-0024-Dm, Steven Darby

p. 85   CMH IMG2016-0321-0029-Dm, Steven Darby

p. 87   Library and Archives Canada, a147732

p. 89   Linda Hall Library of Science, Engineering & Technology

p. 90   © National Maritime Museum, Greenwich, London, BHC1273

p. 92   Photo by Karen Ryan

p. 95   Courtesy the Government of Nunavut / R. W. Park

p. 96   Photo by ullstein bild / ullstein bild via Getty Images

p. 99   Parks Canada / Jonathan Moore, 2014

p. 100 *(top)* Courtesy the Government of Nunavut / R. W. Park

p. 100 *(bottom)* CMH IMG2016-0321-0038-Dm

p. 101 Parks Canada, 2014

p. 102 Parks Canada / Jonathan Moore, 2014

p. 103 Parks Canada / Thierry Boyer, 2016

p. 104 Parks Canada / Thierry Boyer, 2015

p. 105 Parks Canada / Thierry Boyer, 2015

p. 106 *(left)* Parks Canada / Thierry Boyer, 2014

p. 106 *(right)* Parks Canada / Marni Wilson, 2014

p. 107 *(left)* CMH IMG2016-0321-0031-Dm, Steven Darby

p. 107 *(right)* Parks Canada / Marc-André Bernier, 2015

p. 109 Parks Canada, 2017 / Map © 2015 Esri and its licensors, all rights reserved.

p. 111 Parks Canada / Bronwyn Pavey, 2016

p. 115 CMH IMG2016-0321-0016, Steven Darby

p. 116 CMH IMG2016-0321-0019, Steven Darby

p. 117 CMH IMG2016-0321-0015, Steven Darby

p. 118 © National Maritime Museum, Greenwich, London, 9191-007

p. 119 © National Maritime Museum, Greenwich, London, AAA2077

p. 121 *(left)* © National Maritime Museum, Greenwich, London, 9191-008

p. 121 *(right)* © National Maritime Museum, Greenwich, London, AAA2199